Easter things to make and do

Kate Knighton and Leonie Pratt

Designed and illustrated by
Josephine Thompson, Stella Baggott, Katie Lovell, Erica Harrison,
Non Figg, Jan McCafferty and Antonia Miller

Edited by Fiona Watt

Photographs by Howard Allman

Contents

Hen and chicks

1. Pull out lots of pages from old magazines with brown, red, yellow and orange pictures, patterns and textures on them.

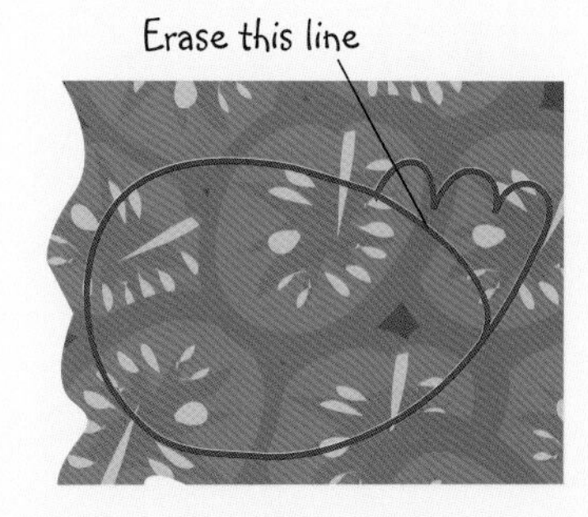

2. Use a pencil to draw a big body, shaped like an egg, on red or brown paper. Add bumps for tail feathers. Then, cut around the outline.

3. Glue the body at one end of a big piece of white paper. Then, cut out a wing from a different shade of brown and glue it on top.

This grass, sky and fence were made first and the hens and chicks glued on top.

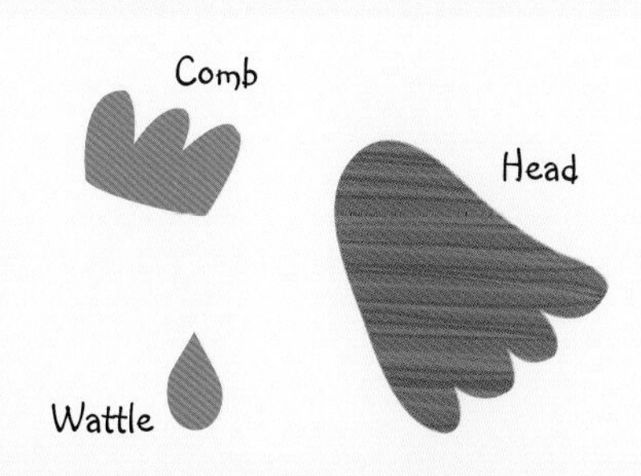

4. Cut out a red crown shape for the hen's comb, and a teardrop for her wattle. Then, cut out a large brown head.

5. Glue the comb and the wattle onto the back of the head. Then, glue the head on so that it overlaps the body.

6. Cut out yellow feet and glue them below the body. Then, cut out some brown feather shapes and glue them at the top of the legs.

7. Add an eye cut from a circle of white paper with a smaller black circle glued on top. Then, cut out a yellow beak and glue it on.

8. To make a chick, cut out a body from yellow paper. Then, add a paler yellow wing, orange feet, an eye and a little red beak.

You could make a line of chicks, with one breaking out of an eggshell, like this.

Easter egg cards

1. To make patterned paper, dip a thick paintbrush into clean water. Then, brush the water all over a piece of thick white paper.

2. While the paper is still wet, blob different shades of bright watery paint on it. The paints will run into each other.

3. While the paint is drying, cut a rectangle from a piece of thick paper. Fold the paper in half to make a card.

4. Cut out four small squares, the same size, from white paper. Arrange them on the card and glue them on, like this.

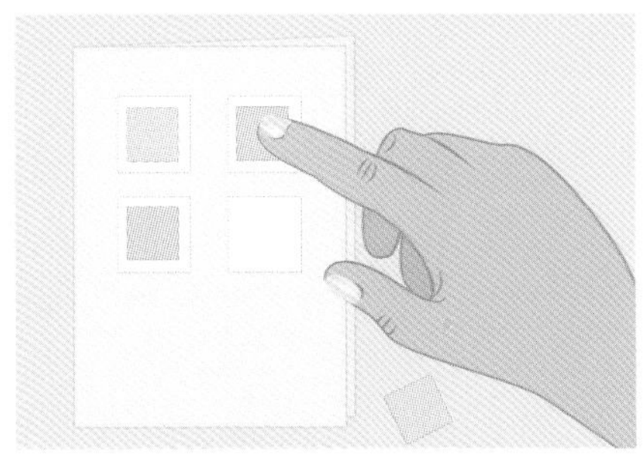

5. Cut four more squares from tissue paper. Make them slightly smaller than the white squares. Glue them on top.

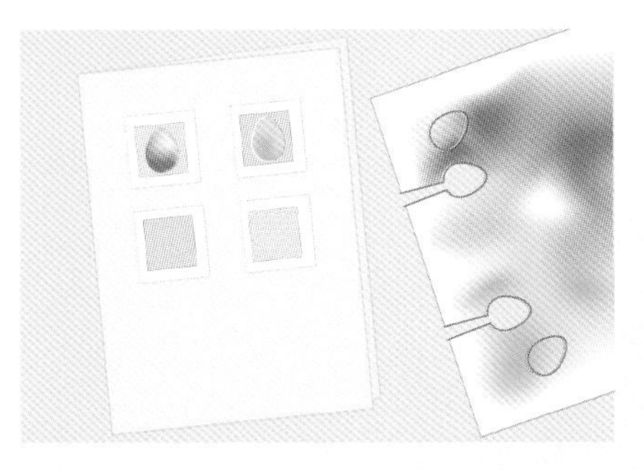

6. Cut out an egg from the patterned paper. Draw around it three times and cut out the eggs. Glue the eggs on top of the squares.

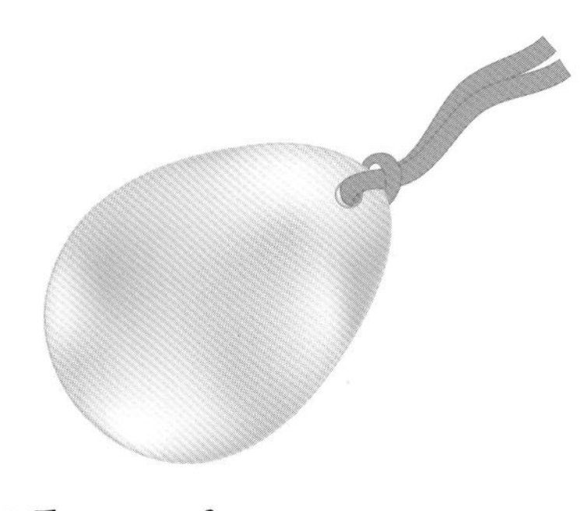

7. For a gift tag, cut an egg from the patterned paper. Punch a hole in the top with a hole puncher and thread some ribbon through.

You could decorate the tags and cards with sequins, bows and glitter.

Use the ideas shown here to make lots of different cards.

Pretty tissue flowers

1. Use a pink pencil to draw a stalk with two leaves. Then, draw a big oval at the top with lots of small petals around it.

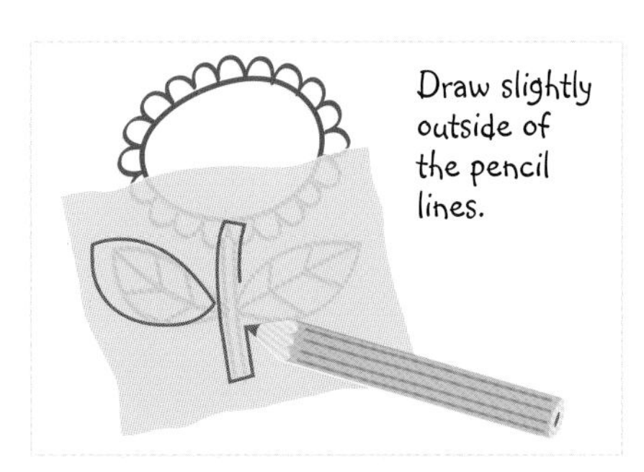

2. Lay some green tissue paper over the stalk and draw around it. Then, draw around the leaves in the same way. Cut them out.

3. Lay pink tissue paper over the oval. Draw around it and cut it out. Then, draw around the petals on yellow paper and cut them out.

4. Brush white glue over the pencil stalk and lay the tissue paper stalk on top. Then, brush some more glue over the top.

5. Then, glue on the leaves, petals and oval. Cut out some little circles of tissue paper and glue them in the middle of the flower.

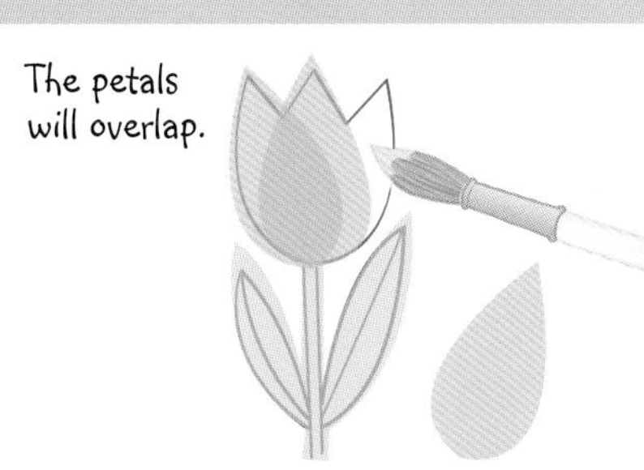

To make a tulip, draw a stalk and leaves. Then, draw a flower shape, like this. Glue on a tissue paper stalk, leaves and three big petals.

Decorated eggs

1. Tap an egg sharply on the rim of a mug to make a crack. Then, use your fingers to carefully break the egg in half over the mug.

2. Wash the eggshells carefully and leave them to dry. Then, hold one half and brush white glue along its cracked edge.

3. Carefully fit the other half on top. Brush more glue around the crack to seal it. Put it in an egg carton to dry.

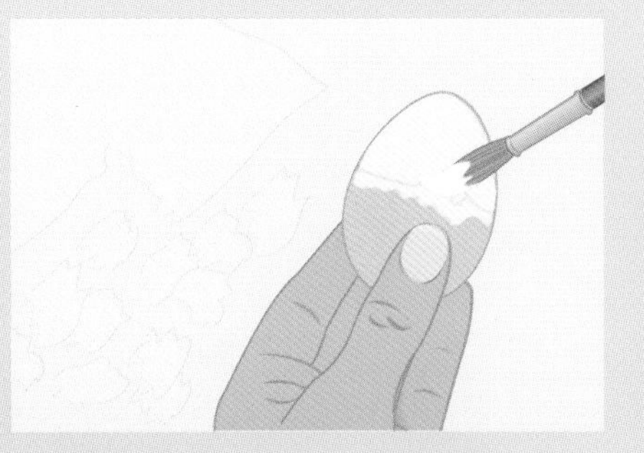

4. Rip a piece of tissue paper into lots of small pieces. Then, brush the top half of the egg with white glue.

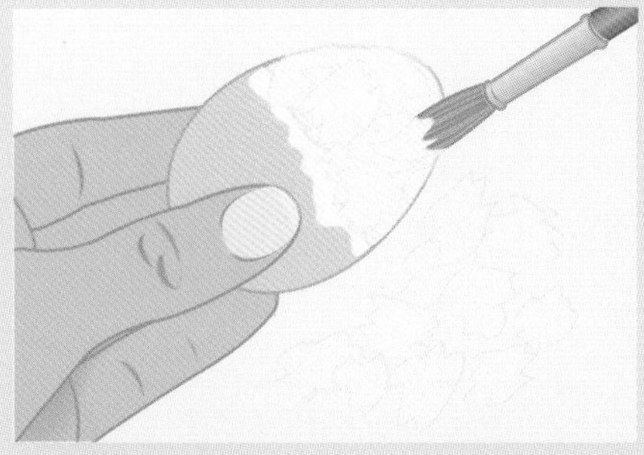

5. Press pieces of tissue paper onto the wet glue. Brush on more glue and tissue paper, until the top half is covered.

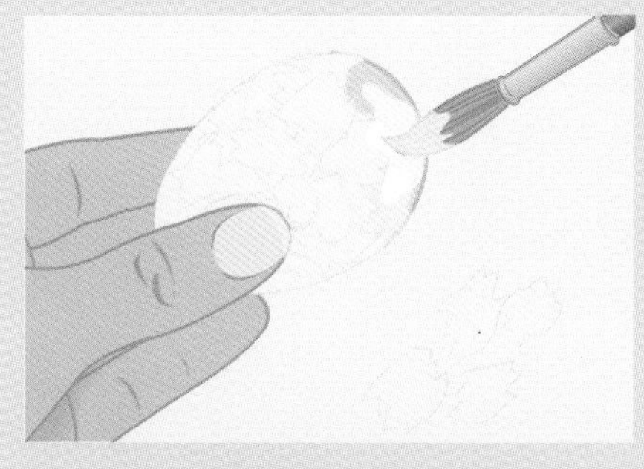

6. Leave the glue to dry. Then, hold the top half and cover the bottom half with tissue paper in the same way. Leave it to dry.

7. Mix some bright paint with a little white glue on an old plate. Paint one half of the egg and leave it to dry. Then, paint the rest.

Decorate one side first, then let it dry.

8. When the paint is dry, mix other shades of paint with white glue. Use a thin paintbrush to decorate your egg with flowers and spots.

Make up patterns of your own or use the ideas shown here.

Easter garland

Tape your garland onto a window, so that it sparkles in the light.

1. Pressing lightly with a pencil, draw a hen on some tissue paper. Use an orange pencil to fill in the comb and the beak.

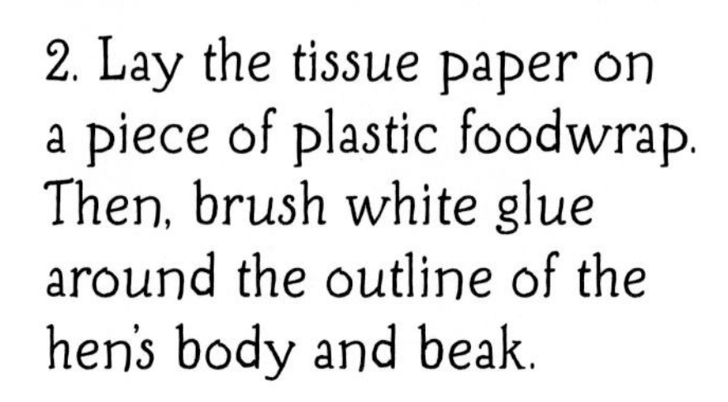

2. Lay the tissue paper on a piece of plastic foodwrap. Then, brush white glue around the outline of the hen's body and beak.

Only glue on the ends of the loop.

3. Cut a long piece of thread and press it into the glue. Cut another piece and make a loop. Then, glue the ends onto the hen's back.

You could trace the shapes on these pages through the tissue paper in step 1.

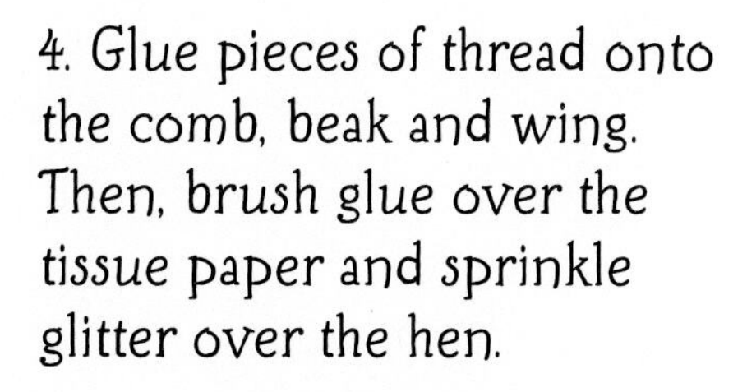

4. Glue pieces of thread onto the comb, beak and wing. Then, brush glue over the tissue paper and sprinkle glitter over the hen.

5. When the glue is dry, peel the tissue paper off the foodwrap. Cut around the hen, taking care not to cut through the loop.

6. Make more shapes in the same way. Thread them onto a long piece of string. Then, use small pieces of tape to secure them.

Fingerprinted bunnies

1. Make two blobs of bright pink paint by mixing red and white paints. Then, mix more white paint into one blob to make it paler pink.

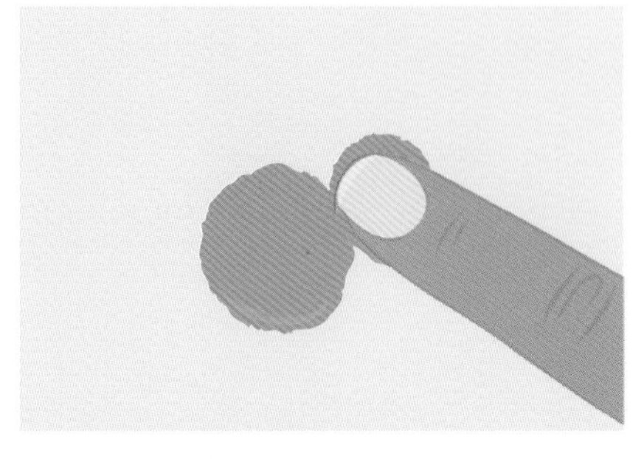

2. Dip a finger into the bright paint and finger paint a bunny's body. Then, finger paint a head on one side of the body.

3. Use your little finger to fingerprint the legs. Then, dip the side of your little finger in the paint and print two long ears.

4. Using the paler paint, fingerprint a patch on the bunny's head, where the nose and mouth will be. Add a print for the tail, too.

5. When the paint is dry, draw a cheek using a pink felt-tip pen. Draw shapes inside the ears and around the legs. Add lines for claws.

6. Use a black felt-tip pen to add dots for eyes. Draw a round nose and add curves for a smiling mouth. Then, draw lines for the whiskers.

You could finger paint a bird's head and body, then add little fingerprints for wings and a tail.
This tree was painted with a brush and left to dry. The leaves, apples and nest were then finger painted on top.

Egg toppers

Pirate hat

1. Cut a piece of paper 15 x 10cm (6 x 4in). Fold it in half so that the short ends are together and the fold is at the top.

2. Bend the paper in half and pinch the corner to make a mark. Unfold the paper and fold the corners into the middle, like this.

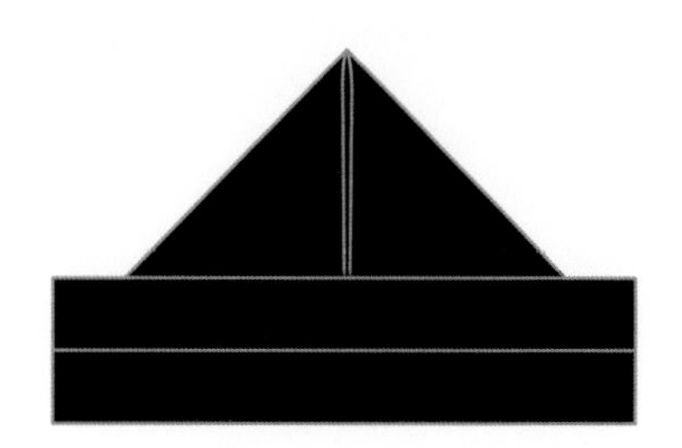

3. Fold up the top layer of paper at the bottom of the hat. Then, turn the hat over and fold the paper on that side up in the same way.

These crowns were cut from shiny paper and decorated with sequins and glitter glue.

Pointed hat

You only need one half for the hat.

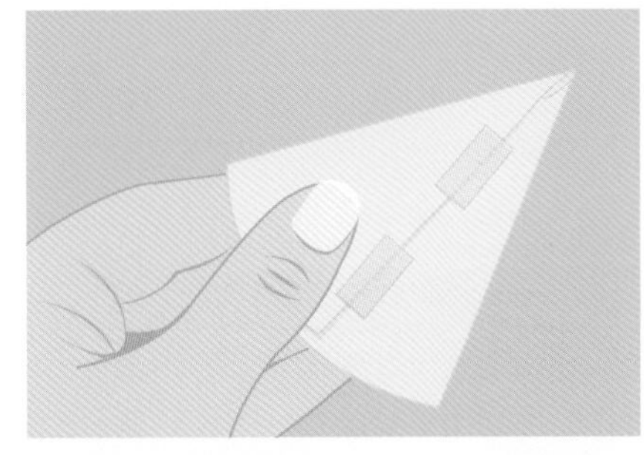

1. Lay a small plate on a piece of paper and draw around it. Cut out the circle and fold it in half. Then, cut along the fold.

2. Bend the paper around so that the corners overlap and make a cone. Then, secure the edges with small pieces of sticky tape.

Crown

Make all the triangles the same size.

Cut a paper strip that will fit around an egg. Draw triangles along the top, then cut them out. Bend the paper around and tape the ends.

This hat is the same as the pirate hat, but turned to the side.

Add star stickers to a pointed hat to make it look like a wizard's hat.

The skull and crossbones on this pirate hat were cut from paper and glued on.

Springtime sheep

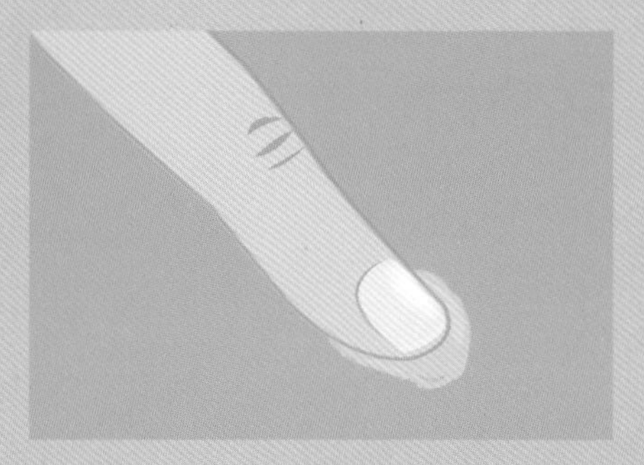

1. Mix a little red paint with white paint. Then, dip your finger into the paint and make a print for a sheep's head on some paper.

Dip your finger into the paint a few times as you print the body.

2. Wash your finger, then dip it into some white paint. Print a tuft of 'hair' on top of the head, then make lots of prints for the body.

3. When the paint is dry, use a paintbrush to add white dots for the eyes. Then, draw the legs using a yellow crayon.

4. Draw around the tuft of hair with a black pen. Add ears and a face. Then, draw around the legs, and add hooves and a tail.

For a butterfly, print four dots with your little finger, draw a crayon line along the middle and add black lines.

Chirpy chicks

Draw two wings at the top of the body for a flying chick.

1. Draw a circle with yellow or orange chalk or a chalk pastel and fill it in. Then, smudge the chalk a little with your fingertip.

2. Use a pencil to draw little lines around the edge of the chick for fluffy feathers. Then, draw two small dots for eyes.

3. Draw a triangle for the beak and fill it in with a red pencil. Draw two legs with three lines for each foot. Then, add wings.

To draw a chick in a nest, draw lines underneath the chick instead of legs. Then, draw smaller lines that crisscross at each side.

You could draw a chick pecking at some corn.

You could decorate an Easter card with some of these chicks.

Spring flowers

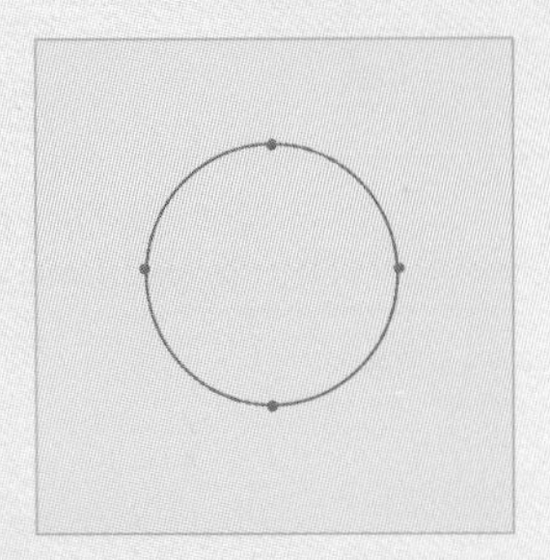

1. Draw around a small lid on a piece of thick paper. Then, draw dots around the circle at the top, bottom, and on either side.

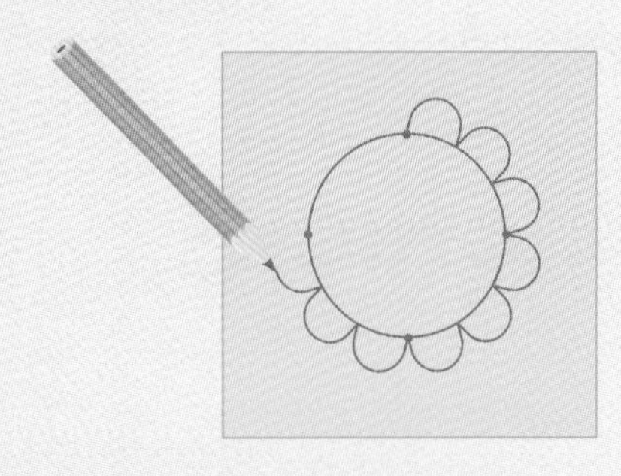

2. Draw three rounded petals between each dot, like this. Try to make all the petals the same size. Then, cut out the flower.

3. Hold a pair of scissors so that the blades are together. Then, pressing hard, run the tip of the scissors along the middle of each petal.

4. Erase all the pencil lines. Then, gently pinch together the edges of each petal along the scored line. This makes the petals 3-D.

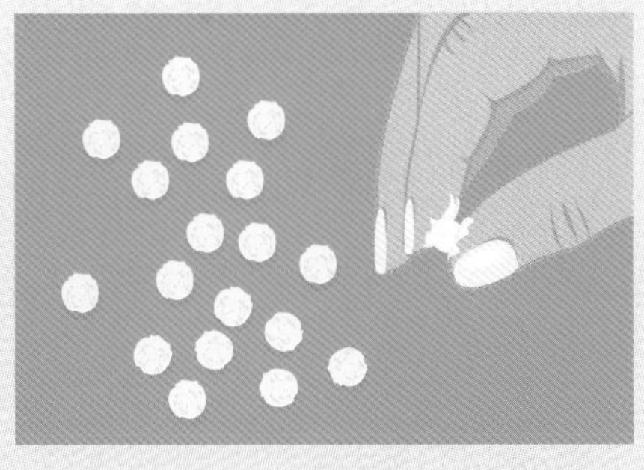

5. Cut some pieces of bright tissue paper and scrunch them into balls. Dip them in white glue, then roll them between your fingers.

These flowers had a circle of bright paper glued in the middle before the balls were glued on.

6. While the glue is still wet, roll the balls in some glitter. Glue the balls in the middle of the flower and leave them to dry.

7. Cut a long strip of thick paper, for the stalk. Fold one edge into the middle. Then, fold the other edge on top and glue them together.

8. For a leaf, fold a small piece of paper in half. Draw half a leaf against the fold, then, keeping the paper folded, cut it out.

9. Crease the fold well, then unfold the leaf. Glue the leaf onto the stalk. Then, tape the stalk onto the back of the flower.

Springtime chicks

1. *Use a pink wax crayon to draw a tree trunk and branches on some thick paper.* Draw a large oval for the top of the tree, too.

2. Draw a nest in the tree. Then, draw the chicks' heads a little way above the top of the nest. Add their wings and bodies.

3. *Use a purple pencil to draw two little triangles on each head for the chicks' beaks.* Then, add the eyes and red cheeks.

4. For a mother bird, *use a wax crayon to draw a circle for the head.* Draw a bigger circle for the body, then add wings and a tail.

5. Draw the beak, eyes, cheek and legs using purple and red pencils. Add spots on the body. Then, draw a worm in the bird's beak.

6. Use pink wax crayons to draw swirls on the trunk and leaves on the tree. Add shapes for flowers, using white and yellow crayons.

7. Fill in your picture using bright watery paints. Then, use a small brush to fill in details such as the leaves and the chicks.

Easter crown

1. Cut a wide strip of thick green paper that fits around your head and overlaps a little. Draw a zig-zag for grass and cut along it.

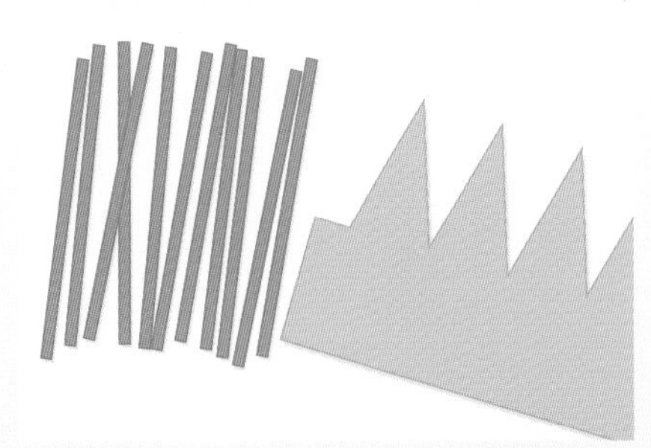

2. Cut out stalks, longer than the height of the crown. You will need enough stalks to make a flower between each blade of grass.

3. Draw flowers with five petals on yellow or orange paper. Then, draw smaller flowers with square ends. Cut out all the flowers.

4. Glue the small flowers onto the bigger ones, so that the petals lie in between the other petals, like this. Bend the little petals up.

5. Tape a stalk to the back of each flower. Then, tape the stalks in between the blades of grass, at slightly different heights.

6. To make bees, cut out four bodies from yellow paper. Draw black stripes and eyes. Then, cut out four wings and glue them to the backs.

7. Cut out four long thin stalks from green paper. Turn the bees over and tape a stalk onto the back of each one.

8. Tape the bees in between the flowers, but so that they are a bit higher up. Then, cut out some more flowers from white paper.

9. Add a yellow middle to the flowers and glue them on the crown. Then, bend the crown around your head and tape it together.

You could decorate the crown with bugs from the sticker pages, too.

Follow steps 3 and 4 on page 18 to make these flowers 3-D.

Collage butterflies

1. Draw two teardrops on a piece of thick cardboard. Make one a little smaller than the other. Then, cut out the shapes.

2. Lay the big teardrop on a piece of patterned paper or material. Draw around it, then draw around it again, to make two shapes.

3. Lay the small teardrop on a different piece of paper or material and draw around it twice. Then, cut out all four teardrop shapes.

4. Glue the big teardrops onto some thick paper, so that the pointed ends touch. Then, glue the small teardrops on below them.

5. Cut out a shape for the butterfly's body from some thick material. Then, glue the body down the middle of the wings.

You could use some of the ideas on this page to decorate your butterfly.

6. Dip a thin paintbrush in some thick paint, then brush stripes across the body. Paint two dots for eyes, then add long feelers.

7. Cut out two circles from material and glue them onto the ends of the feelers. Then, glue a sequin on top of each circle.

8. Cut two more circles and glue them onto the wings. Draw stars on shiny paper and cut them out. Glue the stars onto the wings, too.

Easter tree decorations

1. To make a chick decoration, cut a piece of thin ribbon or thread. Then, cut six strips of kitchen foil about the length of this book.

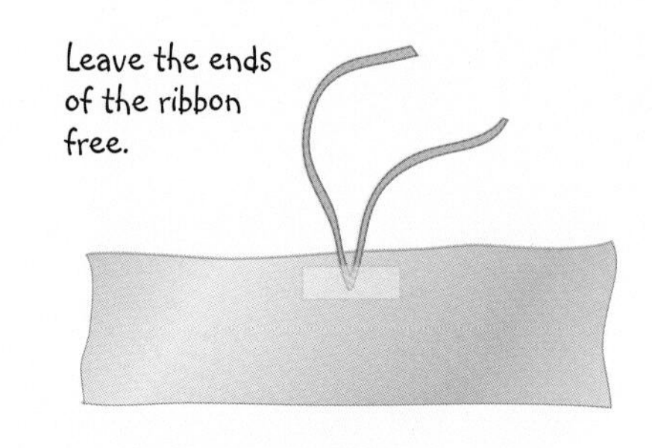

2. Fold the ribbon in half. Lay it on one of the strips of foil and tape it. Then, scrunch the foil into an egg shape around the ribbon.

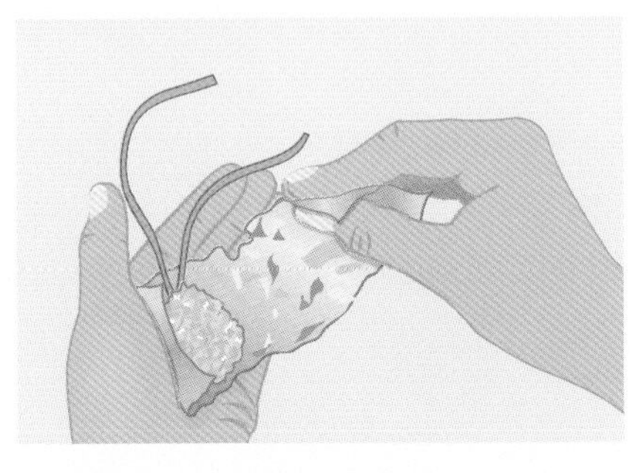

3. Wrap another foil strip around the egg. Then, use your fingers to squeeze and press it to make it into a more solid egg shape.

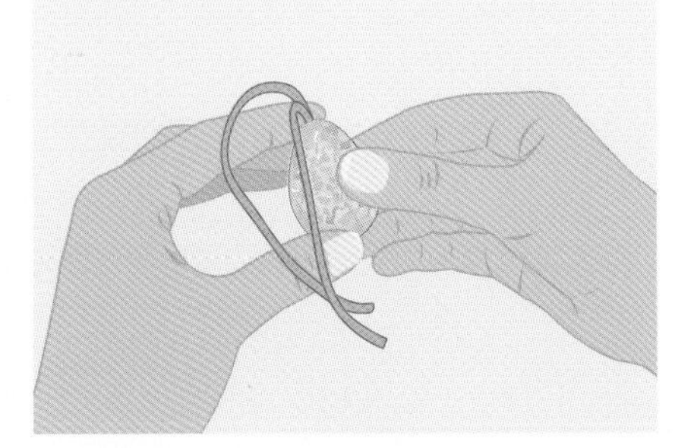

4. Wrap the other foil strips around the egg. Squeeze and press the shape until it is the size you want your chick to be.

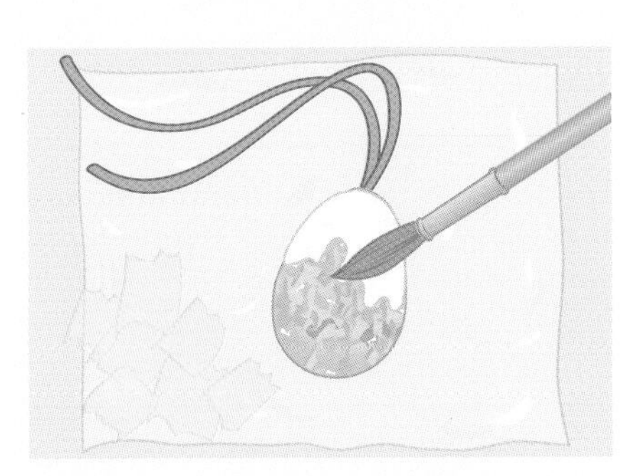

5. Rip a piece of yellow tissue paper into small pieces. Lay the chick on plastic foodwrap, then brush part of it with white glue.

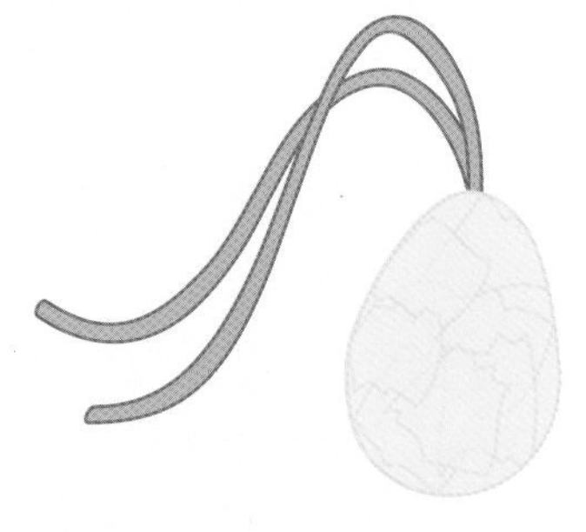

6. Press pieces of tissue paper onto the wet glue. Then, brush on more glue and press on more paper until the chick is covered.

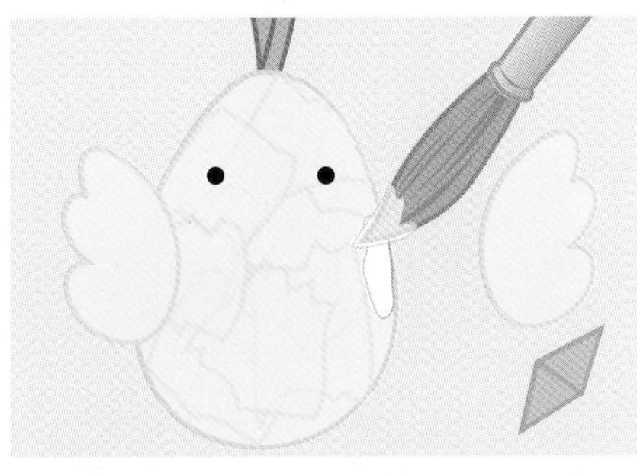

7. When the glue is dry, draw on eyes with a felt-tip pen. Cut out wings and a beak from yellow and orange paper and glue them on.

You could also make Easter eggs covered in different shades of tissue paper.

These branches are made from cardboard, but you could use real ones.

Egg hunt

Draw lots of bunnies and eggs to make a big scene, like this.

1. Mix some watery green paint and brush it all over a piece of paper. When the paint is dry, add some eggs using red and yellow paint.

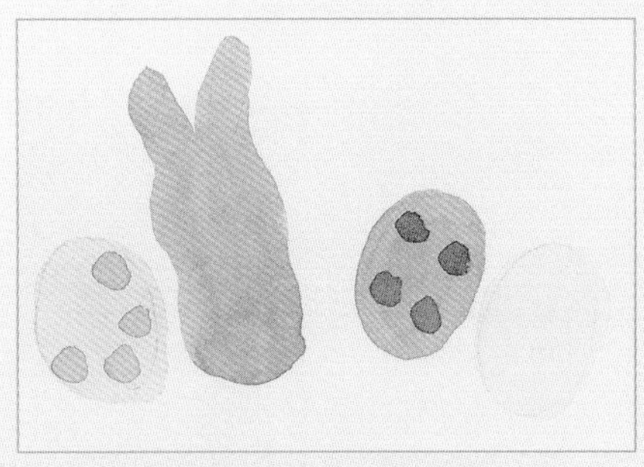

2. When the eggs are dry, add extra blobs of paint to them. Then, use brown paint to paint a bunny's body, head and two long ears.

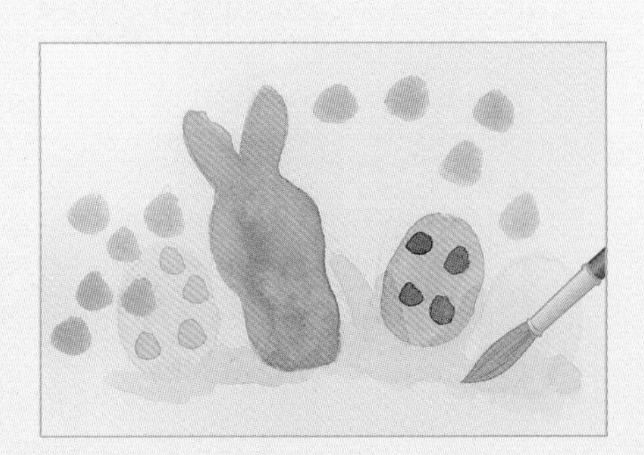

3. Paint smaller spots for flowers around the eggs and bunny. Then, use a darker green to paint grass in front of them, like this.

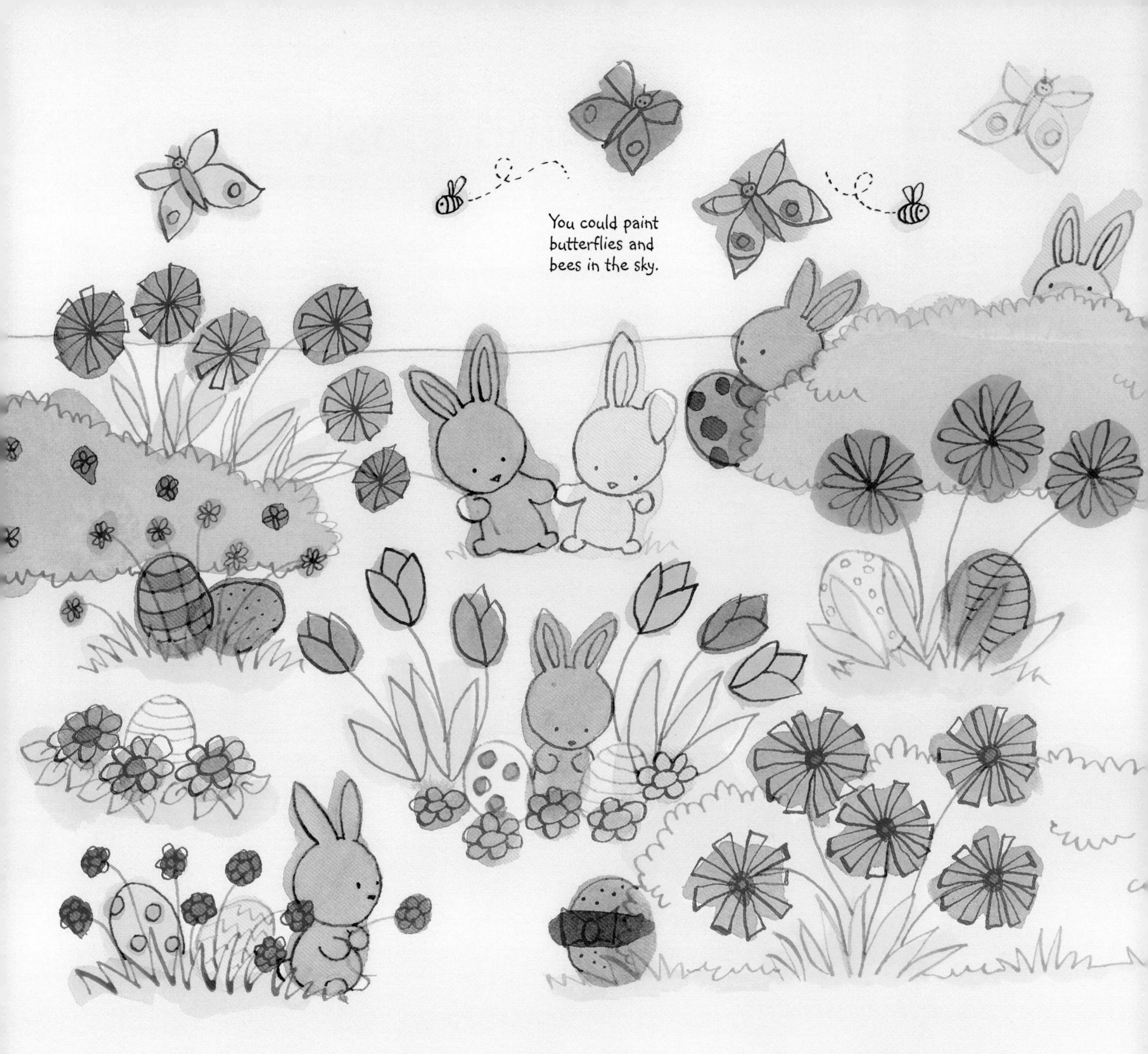

4. When it's dry, use a green felt-tip pen to outline the grass. You don't have to fit the painted shapes exactly. Draw lines for flower stems.

5. Use a bright pen to draw a flower on each spot. Then, decorate the parts of the eggs that aren't hidden by the grass.

6. Use a red felt-tip pen to outline the bunny's head, ears and body, like this. Add small round paws, feet and draw on a face.

Hanging Easter eggs

1. Pour some paint onto an old plate and mix it with a little water. Then, paint a thick line across a piece of white cardboard.

2. Using different shades of paint, add more thick lines. Then, paint lots of thin lines between the thick ones. Leave it to dry.

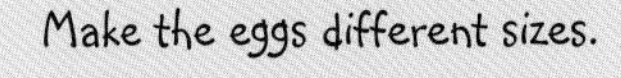

Make the eggs different sizes.

3. Paint stripes in the same way on the other side of the cardboard. When the paint is dry, draw three eggs at the top of the cardboard.

4. Cut out the shapes, then draw around them on the cardboard. Cut these out too, so that you have two eggs of each size.

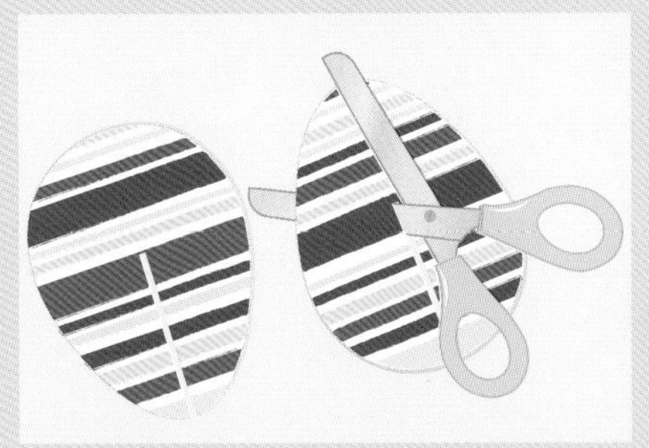

5. Cut a slit, from the top to the middle of one of the eggs. Then, cut a slit from the bottom to the middle of its matching egg, like this.

6. Push the slots together, like this. Cut and slot together the other eggs, too. Then, cut a long piece of thread.

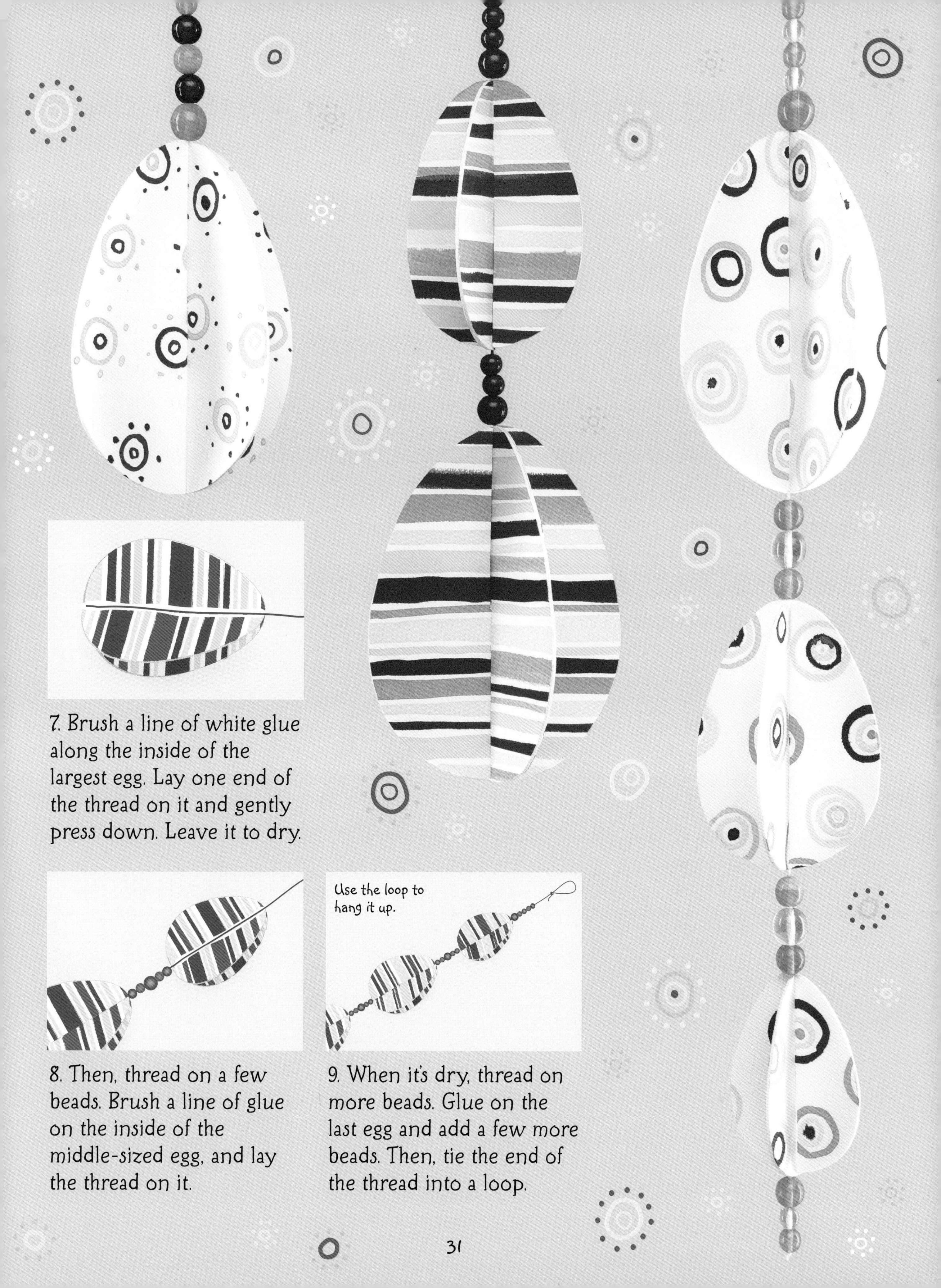

7. Brush a line of white glue along the inside of the largest egg. Lay one end of the thread on it and gently press down. Leave it to dry.

8. Then, thread on a few beads. Brush a line of glue on the inside of the middle-sized egg, and lay the thread on it.

9. When it's dry, thread on more beads. Glue on the last egg and add a few more beads. Then, tie the end of the thread into a loop.

Painted daffodils

1. Use a paintbrush to brush water over a piece of paper. While the paper is wet, use watery yellow paint to paint six petals.

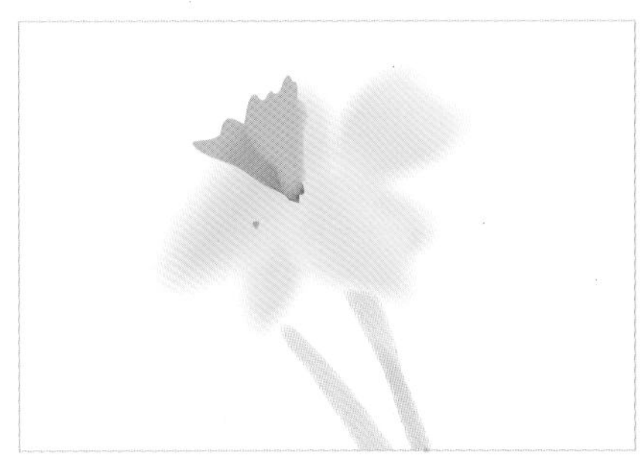

2. When the paint is dry, paint a thin green stalk and a long leaf. Use orange paint to paint a cone shape in the middle of the petals, too.

3. Leave the paint to dry. Then, use an orange pencil to draw a zig-zag shape along the top of the orange cone.

You could paint lots of these daffodils on an Easter card.

Photographic manipulation by John Russell
This edition first published in 2013 by Usborne Publishing Ltd., 83-85 Saffron Hill, London, EC1N 8RT, England www.usborne.com

This edition first published in America in 2013. UE. Printed in Malaysia.